Specials!

Islam

Christine Moorcroft

Acknowledgements

Poems: p18 *Important Notice* by Philip Waddell from *The Works 2: Poems on Every Subject and for Every Occasion* chosen by Brian Moses and Pie Corbett, published by Macmillan Children's Books, 2002.
Baby by George Macdonald. See www.george-macdonald.com/selected_poems.htm#baby.

United Kingdom: Folens Publishers, Apex Business Centre, Boscombe Road, Dunstable, LU5 4RL.
Email: folens@folens.com

Ireland: Folens Publishers, Greenhills Road, Tallaght, Dublin 24.
Email: info@folens.ie

Editor: Joanne Mitchell   Layout artist: Book Matrix   Illustrations: Peter Wilks of SGA
Cover design: Holbrook Design   Cover image: Corbis

First published 2006 by Folens Limited. Reprinted 2007.

British Library Cataloguing in Publication Data. A catalogue record for this publication is available from the British Library.

ISBN 978 1 84303 885 6

Contents

Introduction

Specials! RE Islam provides ten units of work to help students with lower reading abilities to have access to the RE curriculum. Each unit is linked to the QCA scheme of work and to the 5–14 guidelines for RE.

The activities are intended for students whose reading comprehension age is between six and nine. Some activity sheets are more challenging than others; teachers will need to select accordingly.

Each unit contains two to six photocopiable activity sheets. Some of these are pages which provide background information or sources, such as newspaper articles, drawings of artefacts, passages from the Qur'an or prayers, and should be used together with another activity sheet. They can be used in different ways, for example, students could work from them individually, in pairs or in small groups. Where necessary, vocabulary is provided on the activity sheets.

The **Teacher's notes** provide background information which gives guidance to the teacher when using the **Activity sheets**. Also included in the Teacher's notes are:
- **Objectives** (the main skills and knowledge to be learned)
- **Prior knowledge** expected of students to be familiar with already in order to complete the activity sheets.
- **QCA links**
- **Scottish attainment targets**
- **Starter activities** introducing each unit relating it to a previous topic
- Suggestions about using the **Activity sheets**
- **Plenary session** which can be undertaken to recall the key points.

At the end of the book is an **Assessment sheet** to help teachers to monitor students' progress and to provide a useful self-assessment record for the students. They could complete this individually, with the teacher also completing a copy; they can then compare and discuss the two. Alternatively, the students could work in pairs on peer assessments and then compare the outcomes with one another. The assessment sheet can be used to encourage the students to discuss their own progress, consider different points of view and, with guidance, to set targets.

Teacher's notes

The Prophet Muhammad (pbuh)

Objectives

- Know about the time when a religious leader lived and describe some key events in his or her life
- Know about the person's beliefs and teachings
- Reflect on questions about the meaning and purpose of human existence; formulate responses to such questions

Prior knowledge

The students should learn the technical terminology within the study of Islam, for example, faith, idol, prophet and so on. They should also find out the different key beliefs and practices, and use sources to find out about a key figure. Students should be given opportunities to develop skills of interpretation and reflection.

QCA link

Unit 7C Religious figure

Scottish attainment targets

Other world religions
Strand – Beliefs
Level D

Background

Muhammad (pbuh) was a real person who was born in 570 CE in Makkah (which is now in Saudi Arabia), and died in 632 CE. When he was forced to leave Makkah, he moved with his followers to Yathrib (now Madinah – 'City of the Prophet'). The flight from Makkah is known as al-Hijrah. Muhammad (pbuh) and his followers were welcomed in Madinah and a great Muslim community was established there with Muhammad (pbuh) as leader. He helped to build a mosque there. In Islam, prophets are regarded as messengers of God, who are obedient to God, and Muhammad (pbuh) is the last and most important prophet.

Starter activity

Show the students the name of Muhammad (pbuh) written with the Arabic calligraphy for 'Peace be upon him'. Ask them what they know about Muhammad (pbuh). What do they know about the symbol following his name?

Activity sheets

'What do we know about Muhammad (pbuh)?' Ask the students to jot down three things they know about Muhammad (pbuh). This need not be in the form of sentences; it could be in single words. Encourage them to think about any stories or prayers they have heard and about anything they have seen or heard in their local community. Encourage them to tell their group why they wrote each word. Each group could write on a large sheet of paper the four words they think best describe Muhammad (pbuh). Invite a spokesperson from each group to tell the others why they chose these words. Introduce the word 'prophet'.

'Prophets'. Ask the students what they know about prophets. Together, read the passages on the activity sheet and discuss what they mean. The students should then answer the questions.

'Thinking about life' invites the students to reflect on events in their neighbourhood. No names should be mentioned in connection with misdeeds – just the actions themselves. In pairs, the students could discuss what they like and dislike about what goes on around them. When they have completed the table, ask them if they think anything can be done about the actions which harm people or property or make the place unpleasant. Who can do something about it?

'Meditating and praying'. Together, read the information about the early life of Muhammad (pbuh). Ask the students what impression this gives of him. They should write down what his thoughts might have been when he was in the cave.

'Taking action'. Ask the students to read the activity sheet, giving more information about the life of Muhammad (pbuh). Explain that he did not attempt to go out alone in his attempts to teach people about God, but began by enlisting the support of his family and friends. Discuss why some people opposed him. Draw out that he was able to influence people and that many respected him; he had a group of loyal friends and, although there was opposition in his home town, he had strong support in Madinah. The students should complete the chart.

Plenary

Ask the students to look at their responses to 'What do we know about Muhammad (pbuh)?' What can they now add to them? Discuss what they have learned about prophets and Muhammad (pbuh).

What do we know about Muhammad (pbuh)?

☞ Write three things you know about Muhammad (pbuh) in the boxes below.
Discuss your answers with your group.

1.

2.

3.

☞ What do you think made Muhammad (pbuh) special?

_____

_____

_____

_____

_____

_____

Prophets

These passages from the Qur'an, the holy book of Islam, are about prophets.

☞ Read them with a partner. Discuss what they mean. Use them to help you to answer the questions.

a) We send the messengers only to give good news and to warn, so those who believe and mend their lives need not fear.
6:48

b) Did not a messenger come to you, setting forth my signs to you and warning you?
6:130

c) We sent not a messenger except to teach in the language of his own people, in order to make things clear to them.
14:4

d) Their messengers said to them:
'True we are human
like yourselves, but Allah
grants his grace to those of his
servants as he pleases.
It is not for us to bring to you
an authority except as Allah permits.'
14:11

Were prophets humans or spirits? _____

How could someone become a prophet? _____

What was the job of a prophet? _____

How did God make sure that people understood what a prophet taught them?

_____

Which prophet do you think passage b is about? Explain your answer.

_____

_____

_____

Thinking about life

☞ Work with a partner. Think about what goes on all the time in your neighbourhood and in your town or city. What good things are happening? What bad things are happening?

List these on the table.

Good things happening	Bad things happening

☞ Think about one bad thing you would like to change _____

How could you help to change this? _____

_____

_____

_____

_____

Meditating and praying

Muhammad (pbuh) was born in Makkah in 570 CE. His father died before he was born. His mother died when he was six.

His uncle looked after him. When he was old enough, he began to work with his uncle. People liked to deal with him because he was honest. There were many dishonest traders who cheated people.

Muhammad (pbuh) saw that most of the people in Makkah had given up worshipping God. They had made idols and worshipped them instead. Muhammad (pbuh), his uncle and their family worshipped God.

Muhammad (pbuh) found a cave on Mount Hira, which overlooked Makkah. He used to go to the cave to think and to pray – away from the noise and bustle of the town.

☞ How was Muhammad (pbuh) different from most people in Makkah at that time? List three ways.

1. _____

2. _____

3. _____

☞ What might his thoughts have been when he was in the cave? Write in the thought bubble.

Taking action

Muhammad (pbuh) made up his mind to teach the people of Makkah about God. He began with his family and friends. They listened to him. They went with him when he began to preach to other people.

The religious leaders who worshipped idols wanted to stop Muhammad (pbuh). They went to Abu Talib and asked him to stop his nephew abusing the old gods. Abu Talib asked Muhammad (pbuh) to stop because he did not want trouble. Muhammad (pbuh) said that he must carry on preaching because he knew it was right. His uncle vowed to help him, whatever the danger.

Muhammad's (pbuh) enemies plotted to kill him. One man from each clan was to stab him at the same time, so that Muhammad's (pbuh) clan could not take revenge on any one of them. At dawn one day, they rushed into his house, but his friend, Abu Bakr, had heard of the plot and had taken him to a cave in the mountains.

The plotters followed the trail of Abu Bakr and Muhammad (pbuh), but when they reached the cave, they saw a spider's web stretching right across it. A dove had made a nest and laid some eggs in the middle of the entrance. 'No one can be in here,' said one of the plotters, 'if anyone had gone in, he would have torn the web and broken the eggs.'

They went on to search other caves, but they gave up in the end. Muhammad (pbuh) was safe.

☞ What shows that Muhammad (pbuh) was special?
Underline the key words and phrases.

Why did some people want to kill Muhammad (pbuh)?

_____

Who was looking after him and how do you know?
Copy and complete the table below on a separate piece of paper.

People looking after Muhammad (pbuh)	How I can tell

The life of Muhammad (pbuh)

Objectives

- Know about the time when a religious leader lived and describe some key events in his or her life
- Know about the person's beliefs and teachings
- Reflect on questions about the meaning and purpose of human existence; formulate responses to such questions

Prior knowledge

The students should learn the technical terminology within the study of Islam, for example, Allah, angel, Ka'bah, mosque, prophet and so on. They should also find out the different key beliefs and practices, and use sources to find out about a key figure. Students should be given opportunities to develop skills of interpretation and reflection.

QCA link

Unit 7C Religious figure

Scottish attainment targets

Other world religions
Strand – Beliefs
Level D;
Strand – Sacred writings, stories and key figures
Level D

Background

According to Muslim tradition, an angel spoke to Muhammad (pbuh) several times over the course of 23 years, telling him the words of Allah, which he memorised. Each time, he would recite all the words he had been given so far. He passed them on to his followers, who also memorised them. They became known as the Qur'an (recitation).

Abu Bakr, Muhammad's (pbuh) closest companion, decided that he must preserve the Qur'an. He entrusted the task to Zayed Ibn Thabit, who had been with Muhammad (pbuh) during his last recitation of the Qur'an to the angel. It was in Arabic and, because it is the words of Allah, it must never be changed. It has been translated into many languages but no translation can be regarded as the true Qur'an.

The Night Journey, known as the Ascension of Muhammad (pbuh), is a mystical event which Muslims believe happened in the life of Muhammad (pbuh) and which has affected the daily life of Muslims everywhere.

Starter activity

Show the students the Qur'an. Ask them what they know about it. Ask them how the Qur'an is treated when in use and when it is put away after use. Do they know who wrote it or where it originated?

Activity sheets

'The Night of Power' and 'Reactions'. Together, read the 'The Night of Power' and ask the students how Muhammad's (pbuh) wife might have reacted to the story. Would she have believed him? Why? Draw out what they already know about him – that he was respected for his honesty. What might the holy man, Waraqa, have said? Ask them to consider what they would have thought of the meaning of what happened and what Muhammad (pbuh) had heard. How might it have changed the attitude of the Muslims towards Muhammad (pbuh)? Explain that no one questioned Muhammad's (pbuh) honesty, even though it was a strange story, and that they now knew that he was a holy man and that some realised that he must be a prophet. Discuss what can be learned about the Qur'an from this story (Muslims believe it to be the words of Allah).

'Supporters and enemies'. Ask the students to summarise what they know about the life of Muhammad (pbuh). Explain that he had many supporters and ask what made people support him and believe his words. Why should others be against him? Point out that there were leaders of the idol-worshippers who felt threatened because Muhammad (pbuh) questioned their beliefs and practices; they might have thought he was turning people against them. They felt their power being taken away. The students should complete the chart.

'The Night Journey' and 'Story talk'. Together, read the story of the Night Journey. Ask the students to complete the flow chart, listing the five main events in this story. Ask them what can be learnt about Muslim belief and about Muhammad (pbuh) from this story.

Plenary

Ask the students what they have learned about prophets and Muhammad (pbuh).

The Night of Power

One night, on the 27th day of the month of Ramadan in the year 610 CE, Muhammad (phub) was praying in the cave on Mount Hira. Suddenly a bright light shone on him. He felt that someone was there.

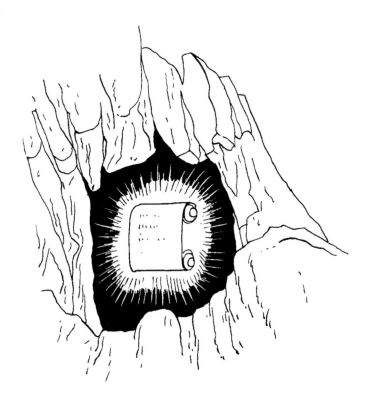

'Who is there?' he asked.

'Read!' said a voice.

Muhammad (pbuh) saw a scroll. There was writing on it. 'I cannot read,' he said. Someone hugged him and then let him go.

'Read!' commanded the voice again.

'But I cannot read,' said Muhammad (pbuh), trembling. Again someone hugged him.

'Read!' commanded the voice once more.

Again Muhammad (pbuh) said, 'I do not know how to read.' For a third time, someone hugged him.

'Read!'

'What shall I read?'

'Read in the name of your Lord who created people from a clot of blood. Read, for your Lord is most gracious. He teaches through the pen. He teaches people what they do not know.'

Muhammad (pbuh) began to read, 'Your Lord is the Creator…'

'These are the words of Allah,' he thought.

He read more. The angel showed him more of Allah's words. Muhammad (pbuh) went home and told his wife Khadijah what had happened. They went to tell a holy man named Waraqa.

This happened on many nights right up to Muhammad's (pbuh) death. He learned all the words and told them to his family and friends. They learned the words by heart. They knew that they must never forget them.

Activity sheet – The life of Muhammad (pbuh)

Reactions

☞ Work with a partner. What do you think Khadijah, Waraqa and Muhammad's (pbuh) friends thought when they heard Muhammad's (pbuh) story?

Write in the thought bubble and the speech bubble.

Think of what you have learned about Muhammad's (pbuh) character, and what his family and friends would have known about him.

Activity sheet – The life of Muhammad (pbuh)

Supporters and enemies

☞ In the chart below, list some of the people who supported Muhammad (pbuh). Explain why they supported him. Who were his enemies? Explain why they opposed him.

Supporters	Reasons	Enemies	Reasons

☞ Imagine someone today preaching to people and trying to convert them to his or her religion. Discuss with a partner how people might react. Write notes about this on a separate piece of paper.

RE Islam

The Night Journey

One night in Makkah in about 620 CE, Muhammad (pbuh) awoke and went to pray at the Sacred Mosque. He fell asleep near the Ka'bah. The angel Jibril woke him and led him back to the mosque. A white animal with wings, larger than a donkey but smaller than a mule, was waiting there. It took Muhammad (pbuh) on its back to Jerusalem with strides stretching as far as the eye could see.

In Jerusalem, the Prophet went to the Al-Aqsa Mosque ('the furthest mosque') to pray. Ibrahim, Musa, Isha and other prophets (pbut) joined him in prayer. Muhammad (pbuh) was offered a jug of wine or a jug of milk. He chose the milk. Jibril said, 'You have chosen the true religion.'

Then Muhammad (pbuh) was taken up into the heavens. At the entrance to each of the heavens, a voice asked Jibril, 'Who are you?'

'Jibril.'

'Who is with you?'

'Muhammad.'

'Has revelation been sent to him?'

'Revelation has been sent to him.'

In each of the heavens, Muhammad (pbuh) was greeted by different prophets. Each of them prayed for his well-being. In the seventh heaven, he met the prophet Ibrahim (pbuh). He was given the revelation of the beliefs of Islam and agreed that Muslims should pray five times a day.

Story talk

☞ List the five main events of the story of the Night Journey in the flow chart below.

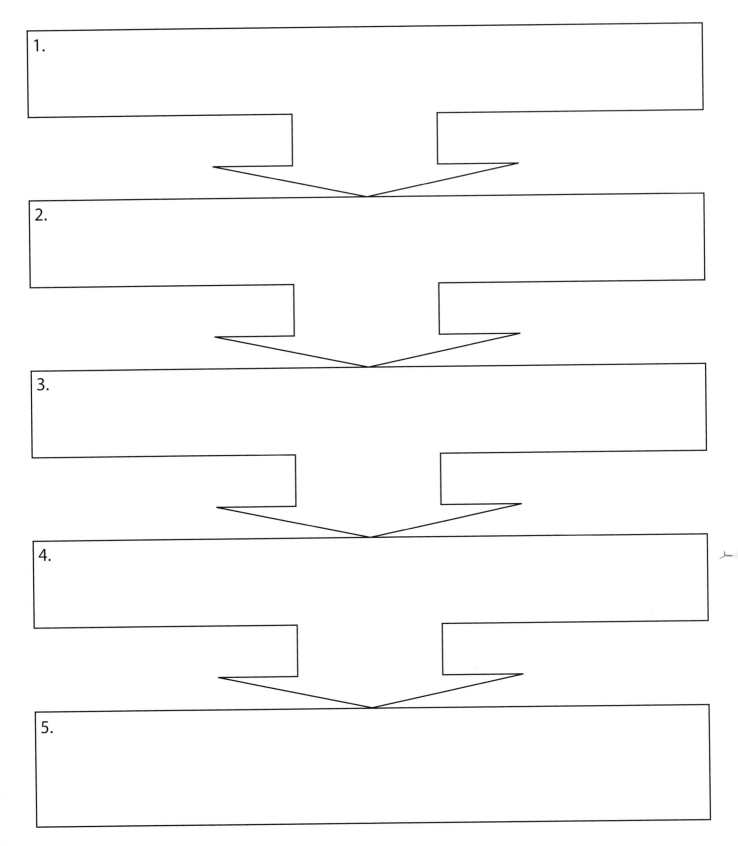

1.

2.

3.

4.

5.

Teacher's notes

Looking after the world

Objectives

- Know about some of the beliefs and teaching of a religion and explain them clearly
- Explain how these affect the lives of believers, making reference to the texts studied
- State an opinion about an environmental issue but recognise that others might hold a different view
- Reflect on ultimate questions about the environment and about the purpose of the world

Prior knowledge

Students should be given opportunities to study the key beliefs of Islam, to make connections between key beliefs and practice and to use religious texts as sources.

QCA link

Unit 7E What are we doing to the environment?

Scottish attainment targets

Personal search
Strand – The natural world
Level D;
Other world religions
Strand – Moral values and attitudes
Level E

Background

The teaching of Islam, laid down in the Qur'an, regards humanity as inseparable from its surroundings. This stems from the 'oneness' of the Creator, from which everything else follows; the whole of creation – the work of one Originator – works within a complex but stable pattern. Creation was designed to function as a whole. Humans are given dominion over the Earth, plants and animals, but with this right comes the responsibility to look after them. Khilafah means stewardship; humans are stewards of the world.

Starter activity

Using an interactive whiteboard, present a slideshow of pictures (identified by numbers) of natural environments. Continue with pictures of industrial landscapes and then land, rivers and lakes polluted in various ways. Give the students time to consider each picture before asking them to respond. Which pictures did they like the best and why? Discuss a picture which shows that humans have damaged the environment. Why do people do this? Is it intentional? Why do they continue with activities they know cause harm? Explain the dilemma of producing the goods and services people need or want and balancing needs and wants against damage to the environment.

Activity sheets

'A message from nature' and 'What is the message?' Before reading the poem *Important Notice* with the students, ask them if they know what a dodo, a quagga and a passenger pigeon are. Why are these animals significant? (All became extinct through direct or indirect actions of people: people hunted them or damaged their food supplies or habitats.) Allow the students a few minutes to reflect on the poem's meaning and the format used by the poet and then ask what types of text are usually written using this type of language. What message does the poet want to communicate? They should answer the questions on 'What is the message?'

'Human effects' encourages the students to consider changes people have made to the area in which they live. After they have listed the good and bad points, discuss why they are good or bad.

'Stewardship'. In pairs, ask the students to read the passages from the Qur'an. Give them time to reflect on the meanings of the passages and then ask them what message the Qur'an gives about the environment. In what way is this message similar to that of the poem *Important Notice*?

'Stewardship in practice' asks the students to choose a Muslim group and to find out about the ways in which this group helps the environment. They should complete the report plan on the activity sheet.

'One small step' asks the students, in groups, to come up with ideas about how they can help the environment, and what they hope the effect of their ideas would be. They should make a list of the actions they could take to achieve their ideas.

Plenary

Ask the students what can be learned from Islam about care for the environment.

A message from nature

Important Notice

World Wildlife Industries sadly announces
that we may soon have to close due to fierce
competition from Human Beings International.

Many of our famous products are already
unavailable including, to name but three, our dodo, quagga and once healthy
passenger pigeon lines.

Currently under threat are many of our
ancient stock of mammals and fishes as well as
birds, reptiles, amphibians and insects.

But even now we could be helped to survive.
Work together with your parents and teachers
to find out how you could all help before it is too late.

And remember – without us and the products
of our other branch, World Vegetation Industries,
our world too might soon be without your company.

Let's work together to stay in business.

Mother Nature

Managing Director

Philip Waddell

What is the message?

☞ Read *Important Notice.*

Think about the poem and discuss it with a partner.

Answer these questions:

From whom does the Important Notice come?

_____

What does it say is happening to wildlife? _____

_____

Who or what is causing this? _____

_____

What warning or threat does it give? _____

_____

Who does it say can save wildlife and humankind? _____

_____

How? _____

_____

Give some examples of what you think can be done.

_____

_____

_____

_____

_____

_____

Human effects

☞ List some ways in which humans have changed the area where you live.

What is good and what is bad about these changes?

Complete the chart.

Change	Good points	Bad points

☞ With a partner, discuss why people have damaged the environment in this way, why they are still damaging it and why they do things which will damage it in the future. Make notes about your ideas. Use extra paper if you need to.

_____

_____

_____

_____

_____

Activity sheet – Looking after the world

Stewardship

☞ With a partner, read these passages from the Qur'an and discuss what they mean.

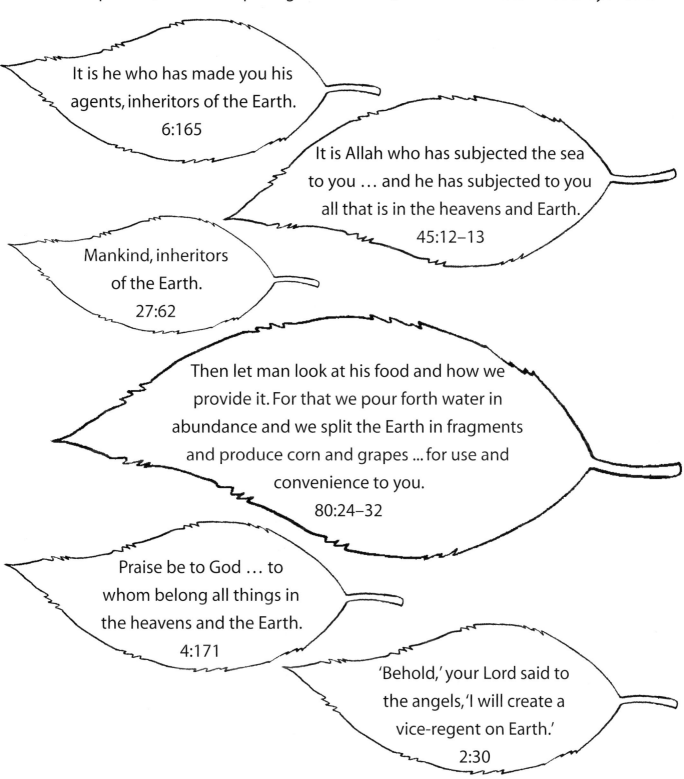

It is he who has made you his agents, inheritors of the Earth.
6:165

It is Allah who has subjected the sea to you … and he has subjected to you all that is in the heavens and Earth.
45:12–13

Mankind, inheritors of the Earth.
27:62

Then let man look at his food and how we provide it. For that we pour forth water in abundance and we split the Earth in fragments and produce corn and grapes … for use and convenience to you.
80:24–32

Praise be to God … to whom belong all things in the heavens and the Earth.
4:171

'Behold,' your Lord said to the angels, 'I will create a vice-regent on Earth.'
2:30

☞ What do these words tell you about responsibility for the Earth?
Make notes on a separate piece of paper.

Activity sheet – Looking after the world

Stewardship in practice

☞ Find out about some ways in which Muslim groups are looking after the environment.

Choose one group to find out more about.

Use this page to plan a report about it.

Name of group:	Country and region or town:

Aim:

List the actions.
Use bullet points.

What the group does:

The effects of these actions:

Past effects:	Effects now being noticed:	Future effects:

What we can learn from the actions of this group:

Activity sheet – Looking after the world

One small step

☞ Working in a group, discuss what you can do to help the environment.

List your ideas on the notepad.

Do not judge any of the ideas until all the suggestions have been collected. Discuss the advantages and disadvantages of each idea. Choose one you know you can do.

_____

What do you hope will be the effect of your actions?

_____

_____

_____

Discuss what you need to do.
Make a list of actions.

Think about...

...where to get information...

...where to get help...

...who can help...

...permission...

_____

_____

_____

_____

_____

Teacher's notes

Muslim belief

Objectives

- Show some knowledge and understanding of the main Muslim beliefs
- Understand the meaning of some religious symbols and use some religious technical language correctly
- Understand what the term 'God' means to Muslims and about the importance of the Qur'an

Prior knowledge

The students should show awareness of some religious beliefs. They should also be given opportunities to read the scriptures of Islam.

QCA link

Unit 8C Beliefs and practice

Scottish attainment targets

Other world religions
Strand – Sacred places, worship and symbols
Level D/E
Strand – Moral values and attitudes
Level D

Background

The flags of many Muslim countries include a crescent moon, stars or both. These have no symbolic origin in Islam but they have been found on coins from 695 CE used by Muslims. The Turks had long been using them as tribal totems; they were used in the decoration of mosques and other buildings and on military flags up to the 15th century. A prayer mat is used for prayer and no other purpose, mainly to create a clean place in which to pray. To avoid any suggestion of idolatry, the decoration never features animals or humans. Many prayer mats incorporate a compass to help users to determine the direction of Makkah – the direction they face for prayer. The prayer on 'A Muslim prayer' is derived from 'A Muslim Prayer for Peace and Religious Tolerance'.

Starter activity

Show the students plaques bearing the names of Allah or Muhammad (pbuh) written in Arabic, which are commonly found in Muslim homes. Also show them car stickers on which are the same names or verses from the Qur'an in Arabic. If they saw a car with these stickers on its windows or a home with plaques like these on the walls, what would this tell them about the owners? Tell them what the words on the stickers or plaques say and explain that the official language of Islam is Arabic, but that not everyone who speaks Arabic is a Muslim.

Activity sheets

'Symbols'. Copy the activity sheet onto an OHT. Ask the students what they notice about the flags. What can they deduce about the countries they come from? (a) Algeria; b) Azerbaijan; c) Comoros; d) Malaysia; e) Maldives; f) Mauritania.) Help them to find these countries on a map of the world. In what part of the world are they? Ask them to work as a group, sharing the work of finding out more about each country, including the colours of the flags. Which colours are the most common? Discuss why. (Green is often used as a symbol of Islam, representing the importance of the natural world.) Explain that these are all Muslim countries and ask the students to find out about the flags of other Muslim countries, for example, Pakistan, Tunisia, Turkey, Turkmenistan and Uzbekistan.

'Prayer mat'. Provide some prayer mats and/or photographs of them and discuss why they are used and how they are suitable for Muslim prayer. After the students have completed the chart, discuss the most commonly used decorations. Draw out why no humans or other animals are depicted.

'Writings about God'. Together, read the passages and ask the students to identify what they say about God (what he is like, what he does and what Muslims believe about him). They should complete the chart.

'Rules for life'. Together, read the passages and ask the students to discuss them with a partner. They should write some rules based on the passages.

'Muslim beliefs and teachings'. Ask the students to read the passages from the Qur'an and underline any words they don't know. They should discuss the meaning of these words. In the boxes, ask them to write what each passage tells them about Muslim beliefs and teachings.

Plenary

Discuss what we can learn from artefacts and from the Qur'an about Muslim beliefs.

Activity sheet – Muslim belief

Symbols

Below are the flags of countries where the official religion is Islam.

☞ Label which countries these flags belong to.

Find out about their colours and colour them accurately.

What do they have in common?

Find out about their symbols. Where else do you see these symbols in connection with Islam?

Look at the flags of other Muslim countries.

a)

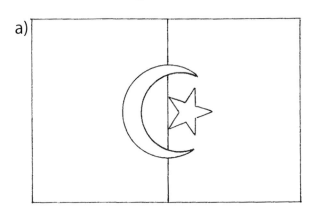

b)

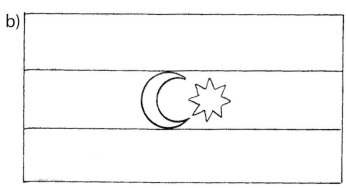

c)

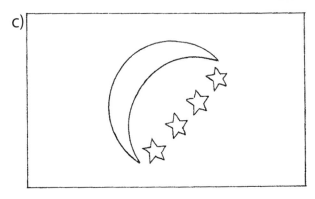

d)

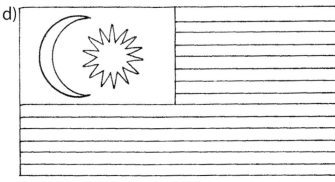

e)

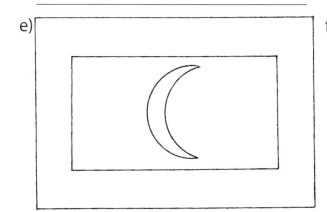

f)

Activity sheet – Muslim belief

Prayer mat

☞ Work with a partner.

Why do you think Muslims use a special mat when they pray?

List all the reasons you can think of.

_____

_____

_____

_____

☞ Look at some Muslim prayer mats.

Record the number of prayer mats on which you see each image.

> There is room for you to add four other images you come across.

Image	No. of prayer mats	Image	No. of prayer mats
flower		mosque	
crescent moon		tree	
leaf		star	

Which types of image do you not see on prayer mats? Why not?

_____

_____

_____

_____

_____

Writings about God

☞ Read these passages from the Qur'an. What can you find out about the Muslim view of God from them? Copy and complete the table below on a separate piece of paper.

d) Your Lord is self-sufficient, full of mercy:
If it were his will
He could destroy you
And in your place appoint others of his choice
As your successors.
6:133

a) It is he who created
The night and the day,
And the sun and the moon:
All the celestial bodies
Swim along,
Each in its rounded course
21:33

e) Allah forgives all his sins:
For he is Oft-Forgiving,
Most Merciful.
39:53

b) Allah is the Lord of
Bounties Unbounded.
3:174

c) Allah is
All-Knowing, All-Wise
4:26

f) To Allah belongs all
That is in the heavens
And on Earth.
Whether you show what is in your minds
Or conceal it, Allah calls you to account for it.
He forgives whom he pleases
And punishes whom he pleases, for Allah has
power over all things.
2:284

Muslim view of God	How I know

Rules for life

☞ Read these passages from the Qur'an to find out about Muslim rules for living.

Discuss them with a partner.

Write some rules based on these passages.

a)
Your Lord has ordered that you worship none but him and show kindness to your parents … Address them in terms of honour.
17:23

c)
When a courteous greeting is offered you, meet it with a greeting still more courteous, or at least of equal courtesy.
4:86

e)
Do not squander your wealth in the manner of the spendthrift.
17:26

b)
Give full measure when you measure, and weigh with a balance that is straight.
17:35

d)
Marry those among you who are single …
Let those who find not the means for marriage keep themselves chaste until Allah gives them means.
24:32–33

f)
Keep away from adultery for it is an indecent deed and an evil way …
Do not take life, which Allah has made sacred – except for just cause.
17:32–33

Rules:

a) _____

b) _____

c) _____

d) _____

e) _____

f) _____

Muslim beliefs and teachings

☞ Read these passages from the Qur'an. What can you find out about Muslim beliefs and teachings. Write in the boxes.

It is he who sends down
rain from the sky;
From it you drink
and out of it grows
the vegetation on which
you feed your cattle.

With it he produces
for you corn, olives,
date-palms, grapes
and every kind of fruit.
Truly this is a sign
for those who give thought.
(16:10-11)

Allah knows what you hide
and what you show.
(16:19)

If Allah so willed,
he could make you all one people:
But he leaves straying whoever he pleases
And he guides whoever he pleases,
But you shall surely be called to account
for all your actions.
(16:93)

Teacher's notes

Muslim beliefs and practice

Objectives

- Show some knowledge and understanding of the main Muslim beliefs
- Understand how religion can affect people's actions
- Identify the beliefs of others

Prior knowledge

The students should show awareness of some religious beliefs. They should also be given opportunities to develop skills of empathy, interpretation and reflection and to agree and disagree with others in a constructive way.

QCA link

Unit 8C Beliefs and practice

Scottish attainment targets

Other world religions
Strand – Moral values and attitudes
Level D

Background

The Five Pillars of Islam (basic beliefs and practices of Islam) are 1) Shahada, 2) Salah, 3) Zakah, 4) Sawm, 5) Hajj. There are set times for the five daily prayers, depending on the times of sunset and sunrise: fajr (between first light and sunrise), zuhr (immediately after the sun has passed its highest point in the sky), asr (between mid-afternoon and sunset), maghrib (between sunset and the last light of day) and isha (between darkness and dawn). Most Muslims follow a set series of prayers and actions. In preparation for prayer, they perform ritual washing known as wudu. Muslims are expected to give Zakah, a welfare due of 2.5% of their wealth, to support people in need. This redistributes fairly what Allah has given. Recipients are accepting their due – not charity. Muslims are expected to perform the Hajj at least once in their lives – unless they are prevented by disability, lack of funds or another good reason.

Starter activity

Ask the students about anything they have to do regularly. Tell them that some people's religions require them to carry out particular activities on a regular basis. Explain the meanings of Shahada (Declaration of Faith), Salah (prayer), Zakah (welfare due), Sawm (fasting) and Hajj (pilgrimage to Makkah).

Activity sheets

'Shahada'. Ask the students to list some things they believe in the chart. They should then discuss their beliefs with others and compare which ones they have in common.

'Salah (Prayer)'. Together, read the passages. Ask the students to underline the key words or phrases which tell them about Muslim beliefs about God. They should then complete the chart.

'Sawm (Fasting)' helps the students to consider how fasting affects daily life. Explain that fasting is a shared activity which focuses believers' minds on God. All who fast are on equal terms, whether rich or poor. Ask the students to find out when Ramadan is this year. They should consider how their daily life would change if they had to fast and complete the chart, detailing what they usually do compared to what they would do if they were fasting.

'Hajj (Pilgrimage) (1)'. Ask the students to find out about the route of the Hajj and the symbolic actions performed by the pilgrims. Ask them to match the names and pictures of a place on the route of the Hajj to what it symbolises.

'Hajj (Pilgrimage) (2)' focuses on the relinquishing of worldly comforts during the Hajj. Ask the students to think of items people cannot do without, such as water. Explain that these are necessities, not material items. Ask them to complete the chart for each of the items shown on the activity sheet.

'Zakah (Welfare due)'. Together, read the passages and ask the students to complete the chart to say who should give Zakah and why, who should receive it and the effects of giving. Explain that Zakah is a way of sharing the bounty of God and that, because this is considered to be what is due to everyone, it is not the same as charity; those who receive it are accepting what is their due and can therefore keep their dignity.

Plenary

Ask the students in what ways the Five Pillars of Islam keep Muslims mindful of God and of their faith. Explain that praying five times a day at specific times affects their daily routine, so that they cannot forget their faith.

Activity sheet – Muslim beliefs and practice

Shahada

This Arabic writing is the Shahada. It says 'There is no god but Allah. Muhammad is the messenger of Allah.'

☞ List some things you believe.

> Which beliefs can you prove to be true?
>
> Which beliefs can you support with evidence, although you cannot prove them to be true?
>
> What do you believe without any evidence or proof?

Beliefs I can prove	Beliefs I can support with evidence	Beliefs I cannot prove or support with evidence

Which beliefs do you have in common with others?

_____

_____

_____

Activity sheet – Muslim beliefs and practice

Salah (Prayer)

☞ Read these passages from the Qur'an.

What can you find out from them about prayer? Copy and complete the chart on a separate piece of paper.

Say:'O my Lord!
Grant forgiveness and mercy!
For you are the best of those
who show mercy!
23:118

Establish regular prayers
at the two ends of the day
and at the approaches of the night.
11:114

O, you who believe!
When you prepare for prayer,
wash your faces and your hands
and arms to the elbows.
Rub your heads with water;
wash your feet to the ankles.
5:6

Establish regular prayers
at the sun's decline
till the darkness of the night,
and at the recital of the Qur'an
in morning prayer,
for the recital of dawn is witnessed.
As for the night – keep awake a part of it
as an additional prayer for you.
Soon your Lord will raise you to
a station of praise and glory!
17:78–79

Celebrate the praises of your Lord before the rising of the sun and before its setting.
Celebrate them for part of the hours of the night and at the sides of the day.
20:130

Prayer in Islam		
When	**How**	**What**

RE Islam

....

Sawm (Fasting)

Muslims fast during the holy month of Ramadan.
They do not eat from sunrise until just after sunset.

Ramadan is at the same time every year in the Muslim calendar. The Muslim year is 11 days shorter than a year in the Universal Calendar.

 When is Ramadan this year?

_____

 How would your day change if you had to fast?
Make notes in the table.

Date:		
Time	**What I usually do**	**What I would do if I were fasting**
00.00 – 04.00		
04.00 – 05.00		
05.00 – 06.00		
06.00 – 07.00		
07.00 – 08.00		
08.00 – 09.00		
09.00 – 10.00		
10.00 – 11.00		
11.00 – 12.00		
12.00 – 13.00		
13.00 – 14.00		
14.00 – 15.00		
15.00 – 16.00		
16.00 – 17.00		
17.00 – 18.00		
18.00 – 19.00		
19.00 – 20.00		
20.00 – 21.00		
21.00 – 22.00		
22.00 – 23.00		
23.00 – 00.00		

Hajj (Pilgrimage) (1)

☞ Match each of the names and pictures of a place on the route of the Hajj to what it symbolises. Write the numbers in the boxes.

1. The first place of worship, built by Ibrahim and his son Isma'il on the site of the shrine of Adam and Eve.	2. Hajar, the mother of Ibrahim's son Isma'il, ran backwards and forwards between these two hills looking for a spring in her search for water.	3. The spring which appeared when Isma'il struck his foot on the ground.
4. The plain where Ibrahim took Isma'il to sacrifice him to Allah.	5. The place where the evil spirit Iblis tried to stop Ibrahim obeying Allah.	6. The place where Ibrahim threw stones at the evil spirit.

Mina

Zamzam

The Ka'bah

Muzdalifah

Safa and Marwah

The Plain of Arafat and the Mount of Mercy

RE Islam

Hajj (Pilgrimage) (2)

During the Hajj, Muslims make changes to their way of life. They make a special journey and they give up material things. These are things people buy to make their lives comfortable. They could live without them.

A. Ice cream

B. Sweets

C. Cola

D. Jewellery

E. Television

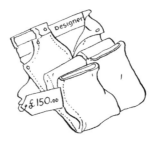

F. Designer clothes

☞ Explain how the things in the pictures are material goods. Think about what they are for. If you did without these things, what could you use instead?

Copy and complete the chart on a separate piece of paper so that you will have more room to fill in the columns.

Item	Purpose	The ways in which it is materialistic	Something which could be used instead
A			
B			
C			
D			
E			
F			

Zakah (Welfare due)

☞ What can you find out from these passages from the Qur'an about Zakah and about giving?

Copy and complete the table below on a separate piece of paper.

> Those who spend their wealth in the cause of Allah and do not follow up their gifts with reminders of their generosity or with injury – their reward is with their Lord.
> 2:262

> Be steadfast in prayer.
> Give Zakah.
> Whatever good you send forth for your souls before you,
> You shall find it with Allah; for Allah sees well all that you can do.
> 2:110

> Charity is for those in need, who … are restricted from travel, and cannot move about in the land seeking trade or work.
> The ignorant man thinks that, because of their modesty, they are free from want …
> Whatever you give to them,
> Allah knows it well.
> 2:273

> Those who believe, and do the deeds of righteousness, and establish regular prayers, and give Zakah, will have their reward with their Lord.
> On them shall be no fear, nor shall they grieve.
> 2:277

> Alms for the poor and needy … for those in bondage and in debt; in the cause of Allah; and for the wayfarer.
> 9:60

> In their wealth there is a due share for the beggar and the deprived.
> 51:19

> Whatever wealth you spend that is good is for parents and kin and orphans and those in want, and for wayfarers and whatever you do that is good, Allah knows it well.
> 2:215

People who should give Zakah	People who should receive Zakah	The effects of giving

RE Islam

Teacher's notes

Everyday life

Objective

- Show some knowledge and understanding of the use of the Qur'an within Islam

Prior knowledge

The students should show awareness of some religious beliefs. They should also be given opportunities to develop skills of empathy, interpretation and reflection and to agree and disagree with others in a constructive way.

QCA link

Unit 8C Beliefs and practice

Scottish attainment targets

Other world religions
Strand – Celebrations, festival, ceremonies and customs
Level C;
Strand – Sacred writings, stories and key figures
Level C

Background

The Qur'an tells Muslims to be courteous to one another and gives some explicit instructions (see 4:86, 24:27–29, 58–61, 49:11). It emphasises the duty to be kind to parents (see 17:23, 29:8, 31:14, 46:15–18). It does not give explicit instruction about clothing but requires believers to dress and behave in a modest way (see 'Muslim dress sense'). This is interpreted slightly differently by different groups of Muslims. Few Muslim women wear clothes which expose their legs or arms and most cover their hair in public. Some cover their faces, too. 'Halal' refers to foods which are suitable for Muslims. Forbidden foods are referred to as 'haram'; they include any food from pigs; animals which have died from diseases or other natural causes, in accidents or killed by other animals; flesh-eating animals or animals which have been offered to idols; blood and alcohol. Halal killing of animals involves one cut with a sharp knife, handling the animal with care, so that it does not know that it is about to die, preventing it from seeing or hearing other animals dying and invoking the name of Allah. The Qur'an gives guidance about this and about what to eat (see 2:168, 172–173; 5:1, 3–5 87–88; 6:118–119, 121, 145–146; 16:114–115).

Starter activity

Invite volunteers to talk about what influences some of the decisions they make about everyday behaviour, such as greeting people, behaviour in other people's homes or choosing what to eat or what to wear. Invite them to talk about situations in which they did not do what they wanted to do or felt like doing at the time. What stopped them? Did they follow any rules? Tell them that they are going to find out about some of the rules which devout Muslims follow in their everyday life.

Activity sheets

'Behaviour'. The students should work in pairs. They could begin by discussing as many options as possible for each situation and listing only those they think are acceptable, before selecting the best. Afterwards, ask them about the options they rejected and why. What influenced them?

'Dress sense'. Ask the students to look at the outfits depicted and to decide which ones they would wear on a hot summer's day to go to town. Invite feedback after they have completed the activity. What influenced their choices? Fashion? Keeping cool? Looking good? Or something else? They should write rules for choosing what to wear at any time.

'Muslim dress sense'. Ask the students which parts of their bodies they think it is acceptable for boys and for girls to show in public. Encourage them to discuss any differences of opinion and to explain their reasons. Afterwards, ask them to explain why Muslim men and boys dress in particular ways and why women and girls cover most of their bodies in public. Encourage them to list the advantages and disadvantages. The students should look back at the outfits on 'Dress sense' and answer whether they think a Muslim teenager could wear them, giving reasons for their answers.

'Menu'. Encourage the students to discuss their views about killing animals for food. In what ways is Halal killing humane? How does it help to prevent careless killing of animals? The students should look at the menu and choose a meal which a Muslim could enjoy.

Plenary

Ask the students in what ways the Qur'an influences the everyday lives of Muslims. What do they think non-Muslims could learn from this?

Behaviour

☞ With a partner, discuss and write notes about what you would do and say in the following situations.

You arrive at a friend's house.
The door is open.

You meet some friends of
your parents when out shopping.

What made you choose to speak and act as you did?

_____

_____

RE Islam

Dress sense

☞ Which of these outfits are suitable to wear in town in the summer?
Put a tick or a cross in the boxes.

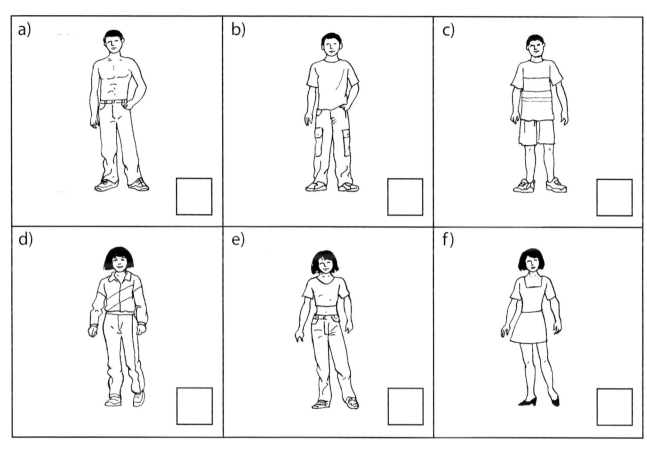

☞ Choose an outfit which is not suitable. Explain why.

_____

_____

_____

☞ Write some rules for choosing what to wear in any season.

_____

_____

_____

_____

Activity sheet – Everyday life

Muslim dress sense

The Qur'an gives Muslims guidance on what to wear.

Men usually cover their bodies at least from the navel to the knees. Women cover their bodies from neck to ankle. Tight or transparent clothes should not be worn.

Guard your eyes and thoughts with rules of modesty in dress and manners.
Commentary 158

Say to believers that they should lower their gaze and guard their modesty, that they should not display their ornaments except as is normal; that they draw their veils over their bosoms and not display their beauty except to their close male relatives.
24:30–31

Believing women should cast their outer garments over themselves when out; that is most convenient that they should be recognised as such and not molested.
33:59

☞ Which outfits from 'Dress sense' could Muslim teenagers wear to go to town? Complete the table.

✓ X

Outfit	Could they wear it?		Reason
	Boy	**Girl**	
a			
b			
c			
d			
e			
f			

Activity sheet – Everyday life

Menu

☞ Choose a meal that a Muslim could enjoy. Tick the boxes.

Menu

Starters

Vegetable soup	☐	Spare ribs	☐
Pea and ham soup	☐	Melon	☐
Prawn cocktail	☐	Grapefruit	☐
Mussels in white wine sauce	☐		

Main courses

Cod and chips	☐	Roast lamb with mint sauce	☐
Curried pork with rice	☐	Mushroom omelette	☐
Baked potato with coleslaw	☐	Crispy duck pancakes	☐

Desserts

Vanilla ice cream	☐	Orange jelly with slices of orange	☐
Chocolate mousse	☐	Lemon tart	☐
Sticky toffee pudding	☐	Cheese and biscuits	☐

Drinks

Milkshake	☐	Tea	☐
Fresh orange juice	☐	Wine	☐
Cola	☐	Coffee	☐

Teacher's notes

A visit to a mosque

Objective

- Describe a mosque using some correct terms and explain how it is used, including the importance of some of its characteristic features

Prior knowledge

The students should learn the technical terminology within the study of Islam. They should also use religious buildings and artefacts as sources.

QCA link

Unit 8E A visit to a place of worship

Scottish attainment targets

Other world religions
Strand – Sacred places, worship and symbols
Level C

Background

The Arabic word for mosque is 'masjid', meaning 'place of prostration'. Most purpose-built mosques have a dome, which is a traditional feature of Islamic design; it is sometimes said to represent the world. Most purpose-built mosques have a minaret ('place of fire' or 'place of light') – a tall, thin, circular tower with an open gallery at the top from which the muadhin makes the adhan (call to prayer). It was originally used as a type of watch tower. The minbar is a platform from which the imam addresses the congregation, usually during Friday prayer. At other times, Muslims pray individually, but Friday prayer is a time of communal worship (for men). Muslims are required to provide a place in which to pray which is pure and clean and not used for any other purpose. A prayer mat creates such an area. The qiblah is the wall which faces Makkah. It has a niche called a mihrab.

Starter activity

Ask the students about any places which are special to them. What makes them special? Focus on places associated with specific activities. Ask them where they would go if they wanted to think about or reflect on anything, for example, to sort out worries or

relationships or to remember someone who has died. What qualities does the place have?

Activity sheets

'Mosque features'. Ask the students how they can tell that a building is a mosque. What special features does it have (inside and outside)? Discuss why it has these features; relate them to the purpose of a mosque and explain how they help Muslims to worship God, for example, there are prayer mats because Muslims stand, kneel and prostrate themselves during worship. They should use the word bank to label the picture of the mosque and then complete the table.

'Mosque sense' helps the students to prepare for a visit to a mosque. Ask them to make notes on the table as to how to behave in a mosque.

'In the mosque' can be used for observations during a visit to a mosque. Ask the students to sit quietly, looking, listening, noticing any smells and experiencing the atmosphere of the mosque.

'Questionnaire' helps the students to prepare for note-taking by articulating what they know and what they want to find out upon their visit to a mosque.

'Mosque detectives' focuses on the similarities and differences between a mosque and any other place of worship the students have visited. Help them to focus on features which are linked with Muslim belief, such as the decoration of windows or walls (no human or animal images, as these could be considered to be idols). Compare this to a mandir, where murtis (representations of gods and goddesses) are an integral part of Hindu worship. Other features to compare include seating or other places where people pray and how these reflect Muslim and other beliefs and practice, the mihrab (indicating the qiblah wall) and why the location of the qiblah is important. Also look for artefacts or the absence of artefacts the students have seen in other places of worship.

'Mosque plan'. Show the students pictures of mosques which are buildings converted from other uses. Have the exteriors been changed much, if at all? Ask what would have to be done to the interior of a local building, such as a house, church or shop, in order to convert it into a mosque. The students should look at the picture of a room on the activity sheet and draw on the plan to show how it could be converted into a mosque.

Plenary

Invite volunteers to choose a feature of a mosque to describe and to explain why it is important.

Activity sheet – A visit to a mosque

Mosque features

☞ Label the picture using the words in the word bank.

Word bank

dome

mihrab

minaret

minbar

prayer mats

qiblah

shoe racks

washbasins

☞ Why does the mosque have these features?

Part of mosque	Symbolism or purpose
dome	
mihrab	
minaret	
minbar	
prayer mats	
qiblah	
shoe racks	
washbasins	

Activity sheet – A visit to a mosque

Mosque sense

☞ How should you behave in a mosque?

Discuss this with your group.

Make notes on the table.

What to wear and what not to wear:	Why:
How to move around the mosque:	Why:
Where to go and what to touch:	Why:

RE Islam

In the mosque

☞ What can you see, hear, smell and feel in the mosque?
Make notes on each notepad.

See

Hear

Smell

Feel

Questionnaire

☞ Plan some questions you will ask about a mosque.

Feature of a mosque	What I know about it	What I want to know	Answer

What people do in a mosque	What I know about it	What I want to know	Answer

Mosque detectives

☞ Compare the mosque with another place of worship.

What similarities and differences can you find?

Write notes in the chart to explain these.

> Think about visits you have made to other places of worship, for example, chapel or church, gurdwara, mandir, synagogue and vihara.

Feature	Mosque	Other place of worship	Similarities and differences	Explanation

☞ Choose one feature of the mosque which is similar to another place of worship.

Choose one feature of the mosque which is different from another place of worship.

Plan a short talk about these.

Make notes on a separate piece of paper.

Mosque plan

☞ How could you convert this
room into a mosque?
Draw on the plan.

Think about
symbols, the important
features of a mosque and
how people use them.

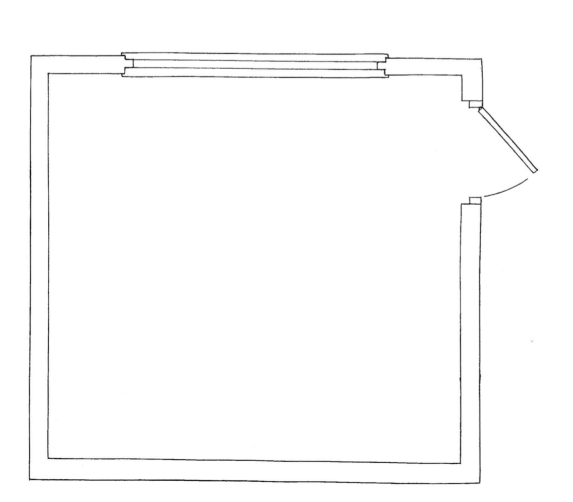

RE Islam

Teacher's notes

Rites of passage

Objective

● Show that they know and understand some Muslim rites of passage and how belonging to a religion affects people's lives at certain times

Prior knowledge

The students should learn the technical terminology within the study of Islam. They should also interpret source materials from faith communities, taking account of different perspectives. Students should be given opportunities to develop skills of empathy, interpretation and reflection and to agree and disagree with others in a constructive way.

QCA link

Unit 9A Where are we going? Rites of passage

Scottish attainment targets

Other world religions
Strand – Celebrations, festivals, ceremonies and customs
Level C

Background

Rites of passage have long been used in different religions and cultures to integrate biological events (birth, reproduction and death) with spiritual experience. They celebrate the connections between an individual and the community. Muslims are encouraged to marry and most Muslim parents introduce their sons and daughters to suitable marriage partners but tend not to force them to marry anyone they do not want to. The ceremony includes legal agreements, for example, conditions about property and money and also the dowry paid by the husband to the wife's family. Muslims, like other religious groups, hold a funeral service for those who die. It is always a burial.

Starter activity

Ask the students to think about memorable occasions in their lives. What made them memorable? Was there a celebration? How were their family and friends involved? Did people send greetings or gifts?

Activity sheets

'Time line'. Ask the students to bring in photographs and memorabilia relating to important events in their lives. They should talk about these. The events could include significant birthdays, starting school, achievements and so on. The students should complete the time line, providing a summary of the most important events in their life.

'New baby'. Together, read the poem *Baby*. Who do the students think is speaking to the baby in the poem? Where do the answers come from? Discuss what the questions and answers tell us about the parents' feelings. Discuss the atmosphere in the poem.

'Muslim baby'. Ask the students how babies are welcomed into families. Ask them to read the instructions for Muslim parents on the birth of a baby and match them to their reason. They could compare these practices to those of another religion, listing the similarities and their reasons.

'All in a name'. Ask the students how their families or other people they know chose names for a baby. Did they name babies after other people? Did they consider the meanings of names? Discuss the influence of religion over the choice of names. On the activity sheet, the students should read the rules for choosing a name for a Muslim baby, go through the list of names for both boys and girls and tick or cross whether they would be allowed.

'Marriage' introduces the idea of marriage. Is it necessary to marry? Discuss the advantages and disadvantages, especially where children are involved. What are the important factors when people marry? List the students' responses on the flip chart. These could be discussed and split into separate lists concerning feelings and practical considerations. The students could discuss how a wife or husband should be chosen and whose opinions should be considered. Emphasise that 'arranged marriage' should not mean 'forced marriage'. Together, read the passages and ask the students to note what the passages tell them about Muslim marriage.

'Death' needs to be introduced sensitively. Ask the students to share their beliefs about what happens after we die. Do they believe in life after death? Do they believe in heaven? Discuss what 'heaven' means. Ask what a funeral is for and how people show respect for the dead and express their feelings of loss.

Plenary

Draw out that ceremonies in Islam, as in other faiths, mark important transitions in people's lives and help them to commemorate these transitions.

Time line

☞ What have been the most important events in your life?

Write summaries of them in the boxes beside the time line.

Link them to the age you were at the time.

Write a heading, your age at the time and anything you did or had to commemmorate the occasion.

14

13

12

11

10

9

8

7

6

5

4

3

2

1

Age

New baby

☞ What feelings does the poem express about a new baby?

Discuss it with a partner.

Write your ideas on a separate piece of paper.

Baby

Where did you come from, baby dear?
Out of the everywhere into here.

Where did you get those eyes so blue?
Out of the sky as I came through.

What makes the light in them sparkle and spin?
Some of the starry spikes left in.

Where did you get that little tear?
I found it waiting when I got here.

What makes your forehead so smooth and high?
A soft hand stroked it as I went by.

What makes your cheek like a warm white rose?
I saw something better than anyone knows.

Whence that three-cornered smile of bliss?
Three angels gave me at once a kiss.

Where did you get this pearly ear?
God spoke, and it came out to hear.

Where did you get those arms and hands?
Love made itself into bonds and bands.

Feet, whence did you come, you darling things?
From the same box as the cherubs' wings.

How did they all just come to be you?
God thought about me, and so I grew.

But how did you come to us, my dear?
God thought about you, and so I am here.

by George MacDonald

Activity sheet – Rites of passage

Muslim baby

☞ Read the instructions for Muslim parents.

Match each instruction to a reason.

1. La illah illa Allah wa Muhammad Abdullu wa rassoulu hu. There is no god but Allah and Muhammad is His servant and prophet. Hayya as Salah. Hayya alai Falah Allahu Akbar. La ilallah. Come to prayer. Come to success. God is great. There is no god but Allah.  Recite the Adhan to the baby as soon as possible after birth.		2.  Rub a softened date or some honey on the baby's tongue.
3. Shave the baby's hair and weigh the hair.	4. Announce the good news to your family and friends.	5. On the seventh day, have two goats or sheep slaughtered for a boy, one for a girl.

Reason	Instruction
So that you can give this weight in silver to charity.	
So that you can share the meat and eat it with family and friends in the Muslim community so that they will all pray for the child.	
So that the first thing the baby will hear is the name of Allah.	
So that they can all share your happiness.	
So that the baby feels good whenever he or she hears the Adhan.	

☞ Compare these practices with those of another religion.

Work with a partner.

On a separate piece of paper, list the similarities and their reasons.

RE Islam

Activity sheet – Rites of passage

All in a name

☞ Read the rules for choosing a Muslim baby's name.

Which names in the lists are suitable?

Rules	
The name should: • be the name of a prophet or holy person, suggest obedience to Allah or suggest a good character.	The name should not: • suggest the worship of idols or anyone other than Allah • be linked with slavery • suggest a bad character.

Girls' names		
Name	**Meaning**	**✓ or X**
A'ishah	Wife of the prophet	
Aairah	Noble, respectful	
Christine	Christian	
Diana	The moon goddess	
Faria	Beautiful, kind, loving	
Fatima	Daughter of the prophet	
Judith	Jewess	
Lakshmi	Goddess – wife of the god Vishnu	
Lucy	A Christian saint	
Tahira	Pure	

Boys' names		
Name	**Meaning**	**✓ or X**
Abdul-Kaliq	Servant of the Creator	
Abdur-Rasool	Slave of the messenger	
Christopher	Christian	
Fadil	Honourable	
George	Farmer/the name of a Christian saint	
Harb	War	
Himar	Donkey	
Joseph	May Jehovah add	
Joshua	Jehovah is salvation	
Kartikeya	Hindu god of war	
Rabah	Profit	

Marriage

☞ Read the passages from the Qur'an with a partner.

What do they tell you about marriage in Islam?

Write notes on a separate piece of paper.

And do not marry the idolatresses until they believe, and certainly a believing maid is better than an idolatress woman, even though she should please you; and do not give marriage to idolaters until they believe, and certainly a believing servant is better than an idolater, even though he should please.
2:221

And marry those among you who are single and those who are fit among your male slaves and your female slaves; if they are needy, Allah will make them free from want out of his grace.
24:32

Wives are an apparel for you, and you are an apparel for them.
2:187

He created mates for you from yourselves that you may find rest in them, and he ordained between you love and mercy.
30:21

Women have rights similar to those of men over them in a just manner...
2:228

Marry women of your choice, two, or three, or four; but if you fear that you shall not be able to deal justly with them, then only one.
4:3

O you men! Surely we have created you of a male and a female, and made you tribes and families that you may know each other; surely the most honourable of you with Allah is the one among you most careful of his duty.
49:13

Activity sheet – Rites of passage

Death

☞ With a partner, discuss different views about what happens to people when they die. Write two different views in the speech bubbles.

a

b

What do you think each of them would want to do with the body of a loved one who has died?

a) _____

because _____

b) _____

because _____

Teacher's notes

Festivals

Objectives

- Show some knowledge and understanding of the main Muslim beliefs and practices and what belonging to a religious community involves
- Understand the meaning of some religious symbols and use some religious technical language correctly
- Identify the beliefs of others

Prior knowledge

The students should show awareness of some religious beliefs and practices, and understanding that belief in God affects people's behaviour. They should be given opportunities to develop skills of empathy, interpretation and reflection and to agree and disagree with others in a constructive way.

QCA link

Unit 8C Beliefs and practice

Scottish attainment targets

Other world religions
Strand – Celebrations, festivals, ceremonies and customs
Level C/E

Background

Id ul-Adha is the final phase of the Hajj. It commemorates the prophet Ibrahim's willingness to submit to the will of Allah in sacrificing his son Isma'il (pbut). Muslims who can afford to do so are required to pay for a sheep, cow or goat to be slaughtered. The meat is either shared with their family and friends or given to people in need. The Islamic calendar (a lunar calendar) is 11 days shorter than the Universal Calendar, so the dates of festivals, which remain the same on the Islamic calendar, move forward by 11 days on the Universal Calendar each year. Id ul-Fitr is a joyful celebration at the end of Ramadan; fasting is forbidden on this day. It begins, traditionally, when the first star is seen in the sky on the day of the new moon at the end of Ramadan.

Starter activity

Ask the students about events they celebrate or commemorate each year. What makes the festival days different? Invite them to talk about what they do and do not do on the special days. They should distinguish between solemn and festive occasions.

Activity sheets

'Id ul-Adha'. Ask the students if they eat meat and how they feel about animals being killed for meat. Remind them of their previous learning about Halal food and ask them in what ways Halal slaughter can be considered humane. Explain that a single cut with a very sharp knife helps to ensure that the animal dies quickly without suffering unnecessarily; preventing it from seeing or hearing other animals being slaughtered prevents distress, and invoking the name of Allah and saying a prayer is intended to make the killing a solemn and serious event – thus reducing indiscriminate slaughter of animals. Ask them to read the sources on the activity sheet and explain why an animal is sacrificed.

'Ramadan'. Together, discuss who should fast and who should not, and why. Explain that it is for healthy adults only – a time of abstinence and not one of suffering, and to remember that the month of Ramadan was when the Qur'an was first revealed to Muhammad (pbuh). The students should answer the questions on the activity sheet. Ask how they would feel after a month of fasting during daylight hours.

'Id ul-Fitr'. Ask the students to find out why the items are important at Id ul-Fitr. (Answers: the star in the sky signifies the end of Ramadan and the start of Id ul-Fitr; Id greetings cards are sent to family and friends ('Id Mubarak' means 'Blessed festival'); the table laden with food signifies the feast at the end of the fast and consists of Halal meat, fruit, traditional sweet foods and drinks such as fruit juice and water (alcohol is forbidden); there is usually communal worship in the prayer hall of the mosque (for men only – women and children usually go into the women's gallery or a separate room).

'Calendar'. The students will need calendars so that they can compare the Muslim calendar with the Universal Calendar in order to find out when the main Muslim festivals take place during the current year.

Plenary

Draw out that most religious festivals commemorate a significant event and that their purpose is to remind people of their faith.

Activity sheet – Festivals

Id ul-Adha

Id ul-Adha is the sacrifice festival held at the end of the Hajj.

Think about ...

... what the sacrifice commemorates ...

... what Muslims are saying to Allah when they sacrifice an animal.

☞ Read sources 1, 2 and 3.

Explain why an animal is sacrificed. Make notes on a separate piece of paper.

---

1. Information about Id ul-Adha

Many Muslims think of Id ul-Adha as sharing what the pilgrims do during the Hajj. In Muslim countries, shops, offices and factories close. Some people choose an animal, such as a sheep, goat, cow or camel, to sacrifice. They take good care of it before it is killed. It must be killed quickly with one cut to the neck from a sharp knife. Nowadays, the animals are usually sent to an abattoir and a prayer is said. The meat is shared among poor people and friends and relatives.

---

2. The story of Ibrahim's sacrifice

When Isma'il was nine years old, his father, Ibrahim, told him about a dream he often had. In the dream, Allah told him to kill Isma'il. They knew it meant that Allah was asking Ibrahim to sacrifice Isma'il. Isma'il said that if this was Allah's will then they must obey. They set off to Mina for the sacrifice. Ibrahim laid Isma'il on the ground and tied his arms and legs. He bent over his son. Sorrow filled his heart. He placed the knife at Isma'il's throat. As he did so, the angel Jibril appeared. He said that Allah was pleased that they were willing to make this sacrifice to please him. He knew that they were devoted servants. He pointed to a lamb which seemed to have come from nowhere: 'Sacrifice this lamb instead,' he said to Ibrahim.

---

3. Passages from the Qur'an

The animal offerings are among the rites decreed by Allah for your own good. You shall mention Allah's name on them while they are standing in line. Once they are offered for sacrifice, you shall eat from them and feed the poor and the needy. This is why we made them submit to you, that you may show your appreciation.
22:36

It is neither their meat nor their blood that reaches Allah: it is your piety that reaches him. He has thus made them subject to you, that you may glorify Allah for his guidance to you and proclaim the good news to all who do right.
22:37

Activity sheet – Festivals

Ramadan

☞ Find out about the fast of Ramadan.

Which of these people should fast during Ramadan?

Put a tick or a cross in each of the boxes and explain your answers on a separate piece of paper.

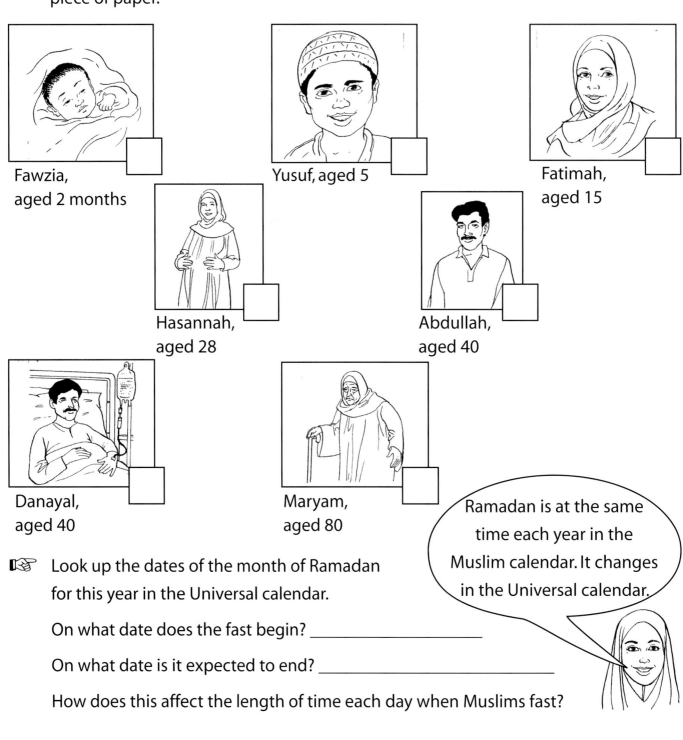

Fawzia, aged 2 months

Yusuf, aged 5

Fatimah, aged 15

Hasannah, aged 28

Abdullah, aged 40

Danayal, aged 40

Maryam, aged 80

Ramadan is at the same time each year in the Muslim calendar. It changes in the Universal calendar.

☞ Look up the dates of the month of Ramadan for this year in the Universal calendar.

On what date does the fast begin? _____

On what date is it expected to end? _____

How does this affect the length of time each day when Muslims fast?

_____

_____

RE Islam © Folens (copiable page)

Activity sheet – Festivals

Id ul-Fitr

☞ Find out why the following are important at Id ul-Fitr and make notes.

Calendar

The Islamic calendar has 354 days. It starts from the Hijrah (the date when Muhammad (pbuh) and his followers moved from Makkah to Madinah). In the Universal Calendar, this was in the year 622 CE.

Muslim festivals are held at the same time each year in the Muslim calendar.

Festival	Date	Festival	Date
Al-Hijra (New Year)	1st Muharram	Id ul-Fitr	1st–4th Shawwal
Ramadan	Entire month of Ramadan	Id ul-Adha (end of Hajj sacrifice)	7th–10th Dhul-Hija

☞ Look up the dates these Muslim festivals will match with in the Universal Calendar for this year, last year and the year before last.
Write the dates on the chart.

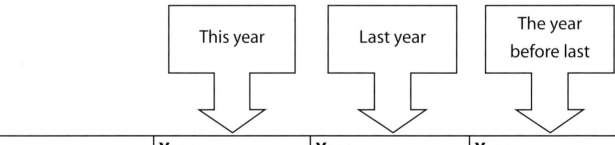

Festival	This year Year: Date:	Last year Year: Date:	The year before last Year: Date:
Al-Hijra			
Ramadan			
Id ul-Fitr			
Id ul-Adha			

What do you notice about the dates of each festival? _____

By how much do they change each year? _____

Why is this? _____

Teacher's notes

Special places

Objectives

- Explain what makes a place special to religious believers
- Show some knowledge of Muslim, Christian and Jewish teaching about harmony, peace and distinctiveness
- Identify and consider questions about human experience, sensitivity and respect for others posed by the sharing of Jerusalem between Muslim, Christian and Jewish communities

Prior knowledge

The students should learn the technical terminology within the study of Islam, for example, the Ka'bah, Hajj, mosque and so on. They should also make connections between key beliefs and practice. Students should be given opportunities to develop skills of empathy, interpretation and reflection and to agree and disagree with others in a constructive way.

QCA link

Unit 9D Why are some places special to religious believers?

Scottish attainment targets

Other world religions
Strand – Sacred places, worship and symbols
Level E

Background

Ka'bah means cube. The Ka'bah is roughly cubic: about 14m high, 10m wide and 15m long. It stands in the courtyard of the Great Mosque in Makkah. At its south-eastern corner is the Black Stone – an oval stone, thought to be a meteorite, about 25cm long, set in a silver frame. Pilgrims try to touch or kiss it as they circle the Ka'bah. A black cloth (the Kiswah) covers the Ka'bah. At the end of the Hajj, the Kiswah is removed and some pieces are given to pilgrims. It is replaced every year. The Ka'bah is the most sacred place for Muslims. Other sacred buildings are the Dome of the Rock and Al-Aqsa mosques in Jerusalem. Jerusalem is a holy place for Christians and Jews as well as Muslims.

Starter activity

Show the students a world map and ask them to locate Saudi Arabia. Show them photographs of Makkah and Madinah and ask them to locate them on a map of Saudi Arabia. On a large-scale map, they could identify Mount Hira, where the Qur'an was revealed to the Prophet Muhammad (pbuh). Do they know why Saudi Arabia is important to Muslims? Remind them of their previous learning about Muhammad (pbuh), who was born and lived in the area now known as Saudi Arabia: he was born in Makkah, migrated with his followers to Madinah and returned to Makkah.

Activity sheets

'Jerusalem' provides a time line with some significant dates in the history of Jerusalem for Christianity, Islam and Judaism. The students can find out more about them and what happened. They will need to complete a key.

'The Ka'bah'. Show the students photographs of the Ka'bah. Help them to find out about it from reference books and the Internet. To develop appreciation that the Ka'bah is a special place, the students could begin by describing places they would save up for a lifetime to visit. These might be important secular places such as football grounds and the homes of pop stars. Have they ever visited a place where they felt that they wanted to keep something from it as a souvenir? Ask the students to complete a factfile about the Ka'bah.

Plenary

Ask the students what they have learned about holy places in Islam. What makes them holy? How can a place be kept sacred, especially when it is shared by people of different faiths? What have they learned about the importance of respect between different cultures and faiths?

Activity sheet – Special places

Jerusalem

☞ Find out about the important events which happened in Jerusalem.
Write them in the boxes linked to the dates on the time line.

Make a key to show which religions they are important for.
Use a different colour for each religion.
Colour the boxes according to the key.

Key	
Christianity	
Islam	
Judaism	

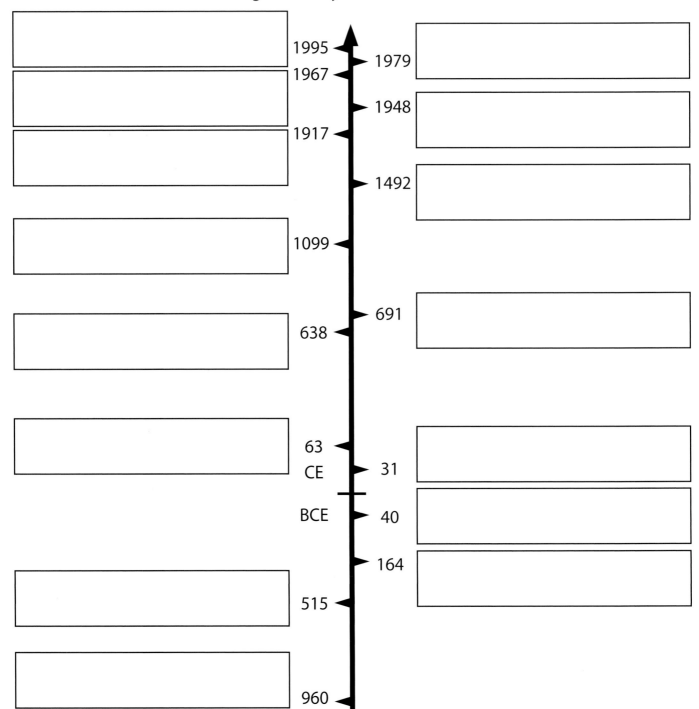

The Ka'bah

☞ Find out as much as you can about the Ka'bah.
Use reference books and the Internet.
Fill in the factfile.

The Ka'bah

Location:

How site was chosen:

First Ka'bah built by:

Rebuilt by:

Shape:

Size:

Colour:

Material:

Special features:

Covering:

How Muslims honour the Ka'bah

Every day:

At least once in their lifetime:

RE Islam

Assessment sheet

Topic _____

At the start

I knew _____

_____

I could _____

_____

Now

I have learned _____

_____

_____

_____

I can _____

_____

Next

I need to find out _____

_____

_____

I need to work on _____

_____

RE Islam